Bible Stories

from the
Old Testament
rewritten especially for children

A Wonderful World

In the beginning, there was nothing at all: no sunshine, no land, no animals, no people. Can you even imagine that? Absolutely nothing!

Then God created heaven and earth, and light so that there could be day and night, and he separated the water from dry land, and covered the land with beautiful plants and trees and lovely green grass. He made the sun to shine during the day and the moon and stars to light up the night sky.

God filled the seas with enormous whales and bright, shiny fish, leaping dolphins and wobbly jellyfish. Then he filled the skies with beautiful birds of every colour imaginable. Next he made animals of all shapes and sizes – spotted cheetahs which could run like the wind, slow tortoises carrying their homes on their back, huge elephants with long trunks and many, many more.

Last of all, God made man and woman and told them to take care of this wonderful world, and all the living creatures on it.

God was pleased with all he had made and done, so on the seventh day, he rested, and made that day a special day, a day to stop working and to give thanks.

Disobeying God

God had made Adam, the very first man, in his own image. He created a beautiful garden for him filled with colourful plants and wonderful trees, and told him to help himself to any fruit except for the fruit from the Tree of Knowledge. But there were plenty of other delicious things to eat!

God brought all the animals and birds to Adam for him to name. But none of the animals were like him, and Adam was lonely, so God created a woman, Eve, to be his special friend and companion. They had no clothes to wear, but that didn't bother them at all.

Now, of all the animals, the most cunning was the snake. One day, he said to Eve, "Why don't you eat from the Tree of Knowledge? The fruit is delicious and it won't harm you!" and the fruit looked so good that Eve picked some and offered it to Adam, too, and they both ate it. At once, they realised they were naked and tried to cover themselves with leaves.

God was very angry. He cursed the snake and sent Adam and Eve away. From now on they would have to work hard to make their own food and clothes. Then he placed an angel with a flaming sword to guard the entrance to the Garden.

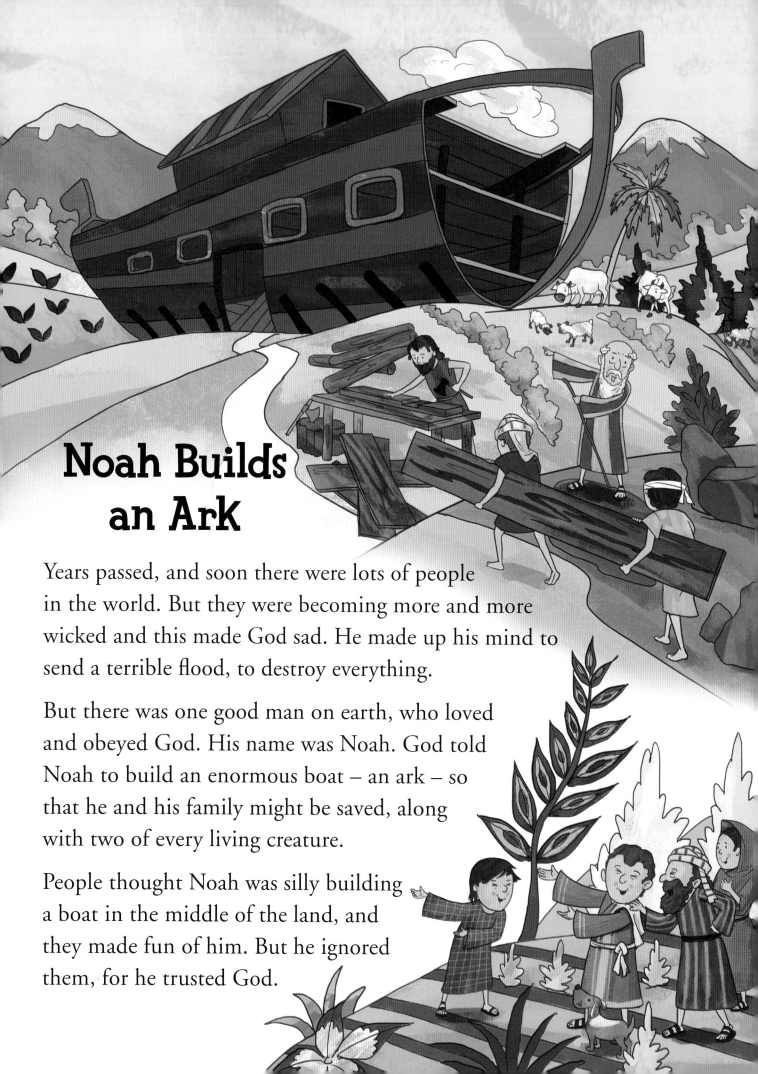

Noah Builds an Ark

Years passed, and soon there were lots of people in the world. But they were becoming more and more wicked and this made God sad. He made up his mind to send a terrible flood, to destroy everything.

But there was one good man on earth, who loved and obeyed God. His name was Noah. God told Noah to build an enormous boat – an ark – so that he and his family might be saved, along with two of every living creature.

People thought Noah was silly building a boat in the middle of the land, and they made fun of him. But he ignored them, for he trusted God.

It took Noah and his three sons a long, long time to build the ark, but when it was finished, Noah, his wife, his sons and their wives, loaded it with food for themselves and the animals. Then God sent the animals to the ark, two by two, one male and one female of every kind of animal and bird that lived upon the earth or flew in the skies.

Once they were all safely in, God closed the door behind them.

The Flood

Now it began to rain. And how it rained! Water poured down from the skies and covered all the land. Every living creature was drowned. All the towns and cities were washed away. But the ark and its precious cargo floated free on a world of water.

For forty days and forty nights it rained. Then, at last, it stopped! After a while, the flood waters began to go down. Noah sent out a dove and when it returned with an olive leaf in its beak, Noah knew that the flood was over, for the trees were growing again.

It was time for Noah and the animals to leave the ark. Noah was filled with gratitude and God promised to never again send such a dreadful flood. He put a beautiful rainbow in the sky to remind everyone of this promise.

The Tower of Babel

To begin with the world had only one language, so everyone could understand everyone else. There came a time when some of Noah's descendants decided to build a city which would be famous throughout the land, with a tower reaching to the heavens.

But God feared they were becoming too proud and vain, so he made them unable to understand one other. Soon a great babble of voices was heard, with everyone speaking in a different language. No one could understand anyone else!

In all the confusion, building stopped and the people scattered far and wide. The tower became known as the Tower of Babel.

The Wonderful Coat

Jacob lived in Canaan. He had twelve sons, but Joseph was his favourite. To show just how much he loved him, Jacob had a wonderful coat made for him, covered with colourful embroidery.

Joseph's brothers were jealous, but what really angered them was when he began telling them of the dreams he had had . . .

"Last night I dreamt we were collecting sheaves of grain, when suddenly my sheaf stood up straight and yours all bowed down before it," Joseph told his brothers.

"What are you saying?" they growled. "That you're going to rule over us some day? Go away!"

Joseph dreamt that the sun, moon and eleven stars were bowing down before him. Even his father was cross when he heard about the latest dream.

"You think your mother and I and your brothers are going to bow down to you? Don't get too big for your boots!"

But Jacob did secretly wonder what Joseph's dream might mean.

Sold into Slavery

Joseph's brothers had had enough – the time had come to get rid of their annoying brother! So one day, when they were out in the fields, the brothers tore off his precious multi-coloured coat and threw him in a deep pit. They would have left him there, but soon they saw a caravan of Ishmaelite traders passing by on their camels on their way to Egypt, and quick as a flash they decided to sell him to the traders. They told his poor father that he had been killed by a wild animal!

In Egypt Joseph was sold to one of Pharaoh's officials, a man named Potiphar. Joseph was clever and hard-working and soon Potiphar placed him in charge of his whole household. But Potiphar's wife told lies about Joseph to her husband, and so it was that poor Joseph found himself thrown into jail!

There Joseph came across Pharaoh's wine steward and his chief baker who had angered Pharaoh. They both had strange dreams and, with the help of God, Joseph was able to explain what the dreams meant. The baker had a dream about birds eating bread from his basket, and Joseph sadly told him that Pharaoh would order his execution, but the wine steward's dream about squeezing grapes into Pharaoh's wine cup meant that he would be pardoned. Joseph asked him to remember how he had helped him when he was released from jail – but he didn't!

Pharaoh's Strange Dream

One night, Pharaoh, the King of Egypt, had a strange dream. He was standing by the Nile when out of the river came seven fat, healthy-looking cows, followed by seven more cows, but these ones were ugly and thin. They ate up the fat cows and looked just as sickly as before! Pharaoh had another dream. In this dream, the seven thin heads of grain swallowed up seven healthy, full heads!

In the morning, Pharaoh sent for all the wise men of Egypt, but no one could tell him what his strange dreams might mean, until the wine steward remembered Joseph, and the slave was brought before Pharaoh.

God helped Joseph to explain the dreams. He told Pharaoh, "The two dreams are one and the same. The seven cows and the seven heads of grain are seven years. The land will be blessed with seven years of healthy crops and fine harvests, but they will be followed by seven years of dreadful famine. You will need to plan very carefully to prepare."

Then Pharaoh replied, "Clearly you are the man for the job! I will put you in charge of my land, and you will be second only to me in all of Egypt!"

So Joseph travelled throughout the land, riding in a fine chariot, to make sure food was put aside for the hard times ahead. Just as he had foretold, for seven years the crops grew better than ever before, and so much grain was put away in storehouses that he gave up counting it! After seven years, the famine began. When people began to run out of food, Joseph opened up the storehouses and sold the corn. No one in Egypt went hungry.

The Brothers Come to Egypt

The famine was bad in Canaan, too, and Jacob and his son's didn't have enough to eat. Jacob sent Joseph's brothers to Egypt to buy grain. Only the youngest brother Benjamin stayed behind. The brothers were brought before Joseph. With his golden chain and fine clothes, they did not recognise him and they bowed own before him. Joseph couldn't help but remember the dreams he had had so long ago!

Joseph wanted to see if his brothers had changed, and so he decided to test them. First he told them to come back with Benjamin. Then, when they did, he sent them off with sacks full of corn, but before they went he hid a silver cup in Benjamin's sack!

The brothers were travelling home when guards came and dragged them back to the palace.

When the cup was found in Benjamin's sack, all the other brothers fell to their knees and begged him

to punish any of them, but not Benjamin, for his father's heart would break!

At this, Joseph knew that his brothers really had changed. He hugged them and told them who he really was. "Don't feel bad," he said. "God sent me to rule in Egypt so you wouldn't starve!"

The brothers were overjoyed. They rushed back to tell their father the good news, and Jacob gathered up his belongings, his herds and flocks, and he and all his family travelled to Egypt. Joseph came to meet him in a great chariot and father and son were joyfully reunited!

The Baby in the Reeds

What could Moses' mother do? Her baby boy was healthy and beautiful, but the ruler of Egypt had ordered all Hebrew baby boys killed! So she wrapped him in a shawl, and placed him in a basket, then lowered it into the water, among the reeds.

By chance, the king's daughter came down to the river and found the basket. "This must be one of the

Hebrew babies," she said softly, and she picked him up and cradled him gently.

Moses' sister was watching from behind some bushes. She bravely stepped forward and offered to fetch someone to nurse the baby. The princess agreed, and Miriam darted off to find her mother, who looked after Moses until he was old enough for the princess to take to the palace.

Plagues!

God sent Moses and his brother Aaron to ask the
king of Egypt, Pharaoh, to let the Hebrews
go free. But Pharaoh refused! So God sent a
series of plagues upon the Egyptians, each more terrible
than the last.

He changed the waters of the Nile into blood, so
that all the fish died, and the air stank. Then he
sent a plague of frogs hopping into every nook and
cranny. Gnats, flies, animal sickness and boils all
followed, one after the other, but still Pharaoh wouldn't change his mind!

Next came thunder and heavy hail which stripped the land, while
lightning struck again and again, and fires blazed! Then came a swarm of
locusts. Nothing green remained in all of Egypt. After this, God sent total
darkness for three whole days.

But now the time had come for the most dreadful plague of all . . .

The Passover

Moses warned Pharaoh that God would pass through the country at midnight and every firstborn son in the land would die, from the son of Pharaoh himself, to the son of the lowliest slave girl, and even the firstborn of the animals as well! Pharaoh would not listen!

Moses told his people that each family must kill a lamb and smear the blood on the door frame, and eat the meat in a special way.

The next day the land was filled with the sound of mourning, for all the first-born sons had died, even Pharaoh's son. But God had passed over the houses of the Israelites and they were spared!

Now the Egyptians couldn't get rid of the Hebrews quick enough, and so Moses and his people prepared to leave Egypt.

Crossing the Red Sea

The Hebrews were terrified! They had travelled across the desert, but now their way was barred by the Red Sea, and Pharaoh had changed his mind and had sent an army after them! "Why did you bring us all this way, just to have us killed or dragged back into slavery?" they cried to Moses.

But Moses did not give up his faith in God. "God will look after us," he said confidently. "And he will crush our enemy."

Then God told Moses to raise his staff and stretch out his hand over the sea to divide the water. Moses stood before the sea and raised his hand,

and all that night the Lord drove the sea back with a strong wind and turned it into dry land. The waters were divided, and the Israelites went through the sea on dry ground, with a wall of water on their right and on their left!

The Egyptians were hard on the heels of the Hebrews and swiftly followed them into the sea along the path that God had made. But God struck them with confusion so that the wheels of the chariots came off and everywhere there was chaos. Then he closed the waters together and the Egyptians were all swept under the sea! Of all that mighty army, there were no survivors – not one single horse, not one single soldier!

The people of Israel, safe on the far shore of the Red Sea, were filled with gratitude and relief and sang and danced in their joy, for they knew that their God was both mighty and merciful and they praised him greatly.

Moses Sees the Promised Land

Moses and the Hebrew people spent many long hard years in the desert. They were hungry and thirsty, but God sent them food and water. He told Moses to go to Mount Sinai. There, on the top of the mountain, God spoke to him, and gave him special instructions to pass on to his people, telling them how they should worship him, and how they should live their lives. These were the Ten Commandments. The people promised to obey – but they didn't always remember!

When Moses was old, he asked God to choose someone to lead the people after his death and God chose Joshua, a good man.

Finally it was time for Moses to leave his people. He climbed a mountain and God showed him the land of Canaan in the distance – the land that had been promised to his ancestors, a land of rich soil and flowing water, full of good things to eat and drink.

Moses died on the mountain. He was a hundred and twenty years old! The people were sad. They knew there would never be another prophet like him, who had spoken with God face to face.

The Walls of Jericho

It was time for the Israelites to take the Promised Land. The people of Jericho laughed at them from behind their strong, high walls. "You'll never get in!" they jeered. But Joshua was unafraid. He knew God would help them.

God told Joshua exactly what to do. Once a day for six days the Israelite army marched quietly around the city, while priests blew on trumpets. On the seventh day, when the trumpets sounded, the Israelites raised a mighty cry, and the city walls trembled and then collapsed before them!

The soldiers charged in and took the city, and the story of how the Lord had helped Joshua take Jericho spread far and wide.

Faithful Ruth

Naomi was moving back to Bethlehem. Her husband and sons had died and she wanted to go home, but she begged her beloved daughters-in-law, Orpah and Ruth, to stay behind, for she was penniless and she knew that her life would be hard.

Orpah and Ruth loved Naomi dearly, and did not want to stay behind, but finally Orpah agreed to go home. Loyal Ruth, however, said earnestly, "Don't ask me to leave! I will go wherever you go. Your people will be my people and your God will be my God!"

So it was that Ruth and Naomi came to Bethlehem. Soon they had no food left, and brave Ruth went out into the fields where workers were harvesting the crops and asked the owner if she could pick up any of the barley that his workers left behind.

Boaz had heard about how loyal Ruth had been to Naomi. He let her work in his fields and told his servants to share their food with her. He even told them to drop some of the barley for her to pick up!

When Ruth returned with a full basket of food and said how kind Boaz had been, Naomi knew that the Lord was looking after them, for Boaz was a relation of hers.

In time, Ruth married Boaz, and when they had a son, there was no happier woman in the whole of Bethlehem than Naomi!

A Stone in a Sling

David was just a shepherd boy. He was the youngest of his family and he had many brothers who were older and stronger than he was. But God had chosen him as the future leader of Israel! The Israelites were at war with the Philistines and the two armies had gathered to do battle. Young David had brought food to his brothers who were fighting in the army.

The Philistines had a mighty champion. His name was Goliath and he was powerful and strong – and ten feet tall! Goliath challenged the Israelites to single combat, but no one dared to fight him. No one, that is, apart from David!

David stood before Goliath. God had been with him when he had protected his sheep from lions and bears, and David knew that God

would be with him now. He stood there with nothing but his staff, a sling, and five stones . . .

Goliath laughed at him, but David fearlessly ran forward, putting a stone in his sling and flinging it with all his might. It hit Goliath on his forehead and when he fell to the ground, David raced up and cut off his head using Goliath's own sword! The Philistines were so shocked that they turned and ran away! The battle had been won by a shepherd boy – and God!

In the Lions' Den

Daniel had an important job in the court of King Darius of Persia. He was an exile from Jerusalem, but the king trusted him. The other officials were jealous. They knew Daniel prayed every day, and they came up with a nasty plan.

They had the king sign an order stating that for thirty days, anyone asking anything of any god or man except the king should be thrown into a den of lions!

Daniel prayed just as he had always done. He would not stop, or even hide what he was doing. His enemies rushed to the king and told him. Darius' heart sank but he could not change the law.

"You have been loyal to your God. I hope he can save you," he said sadly, as Daniel was thrown to the lions!

That evening the king did not sleep a wink. At first light, he rushed down to the pit. "Daniel!" he cried out, more in desperation than hope. "Has your God been able to save you?"

How thrilled and amazed he was when he saw Daniel sitting amongst the lions, completely unharmed, for God had sent an angel to shut the mouths of the lions! "Your God truly is wonderful!" said King Darius, and he ordered that from then on, everyone in the kingdom should respect and honour Daniel's God!

As for the wicked men who had tricked him – they were thrown into the pit themselves – and this time the lions were ruthless!

The Brave Queen

King Xerxes of Persia was looking for a new queen. From all the beautiful young girls of the land, he chose lovely Esther. Esther did not tell him she was a Jew.

The king's advisor Haman hated Jews, especially Esther's cousin, Mordecai. Haman tricked the king into signing a decree that ordered the killing of all Jews. Esther's cousin told her that she had to try to get the king to change his mind.

Esther was frightened. To go before the king without a summons was punishable by death! Only if the king held out his sceptre would the person be spared. But Mordecai sent another message, saying, "Maybe God made you queen precisely so that you can save his people."

Esther was scared, but made up her mind to go to the king. When he saw her, he smiled and held out his golden sceptre, asking her what she wanted.

Esther could not bring herself to ask the king there and then. Instead, she invited him and Haman to a banquet in her rooms.

When the king came to dinner, he offered her anything she wanted – up to half his kingdom! Esther bravely told him that she was a Jew, and she asked him to save her people.

When the king found out how Haman had tricked him, he sent him to the gallows. He couldn't change the decree, but he made another one saying that the Jews would be allowed to defend themselves.

When the Jews were attacked they were able to fight back, and they overcame their enemies. They were saved! And every year the Jewish people celebrate the bravery of beautiful queen Esther.